IS THERE LIFE WITHOUT CATS?

by - TONI GOFFE

CATS ARE WHERE IT'S AT

First published in Great Britain by
Pendulum Gallery Press
56 Ackender Road, Alton, Hants GU34 1JS

© TONI GOFFE 1993

IS THERE LIFE WITHOUT CATS?
ISBN 0-948912-21-9

REPRINTED 1993 1997

PRINTED IN GREAT BRITAIN BY
UNWIN BROTHERS LTD, OLD WOKING, SURREY

CAT INFORMATION SERVICE:
HOW TO ESCAPE FROM AN OVERLOVING HUMAN.

CONCESSION:

LET YOUR HUMAN
PICK YOU UP AND
HOLD YOU FOR A
SHORT TIME...

WHEN FED UP,
TRY WRIGGLING.
IF THIS DOESN'T
WORK. USE THE
FOLLOWING
METHODS OF
ESCAPE.....

FIRST:
THE HOLD
POSITION

ROUTE ONE...   ROUTE TWO...

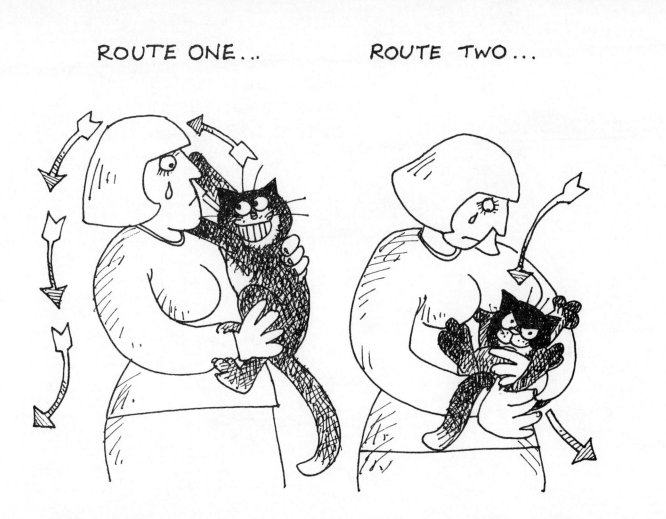

HIS MASTER'S VOICE...

STUFF CATS DO WHEN YOU'RE OUT...

HECTOR, TRYING TO OUTSTARE HIS HUMAN...

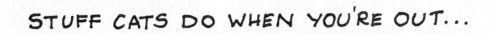

STUFF CATS DO WHEN YOU'RE OUT...

PUSSY IN BOTTLE...

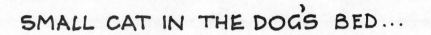

SMALL CAT IN THE DOG'S BED...

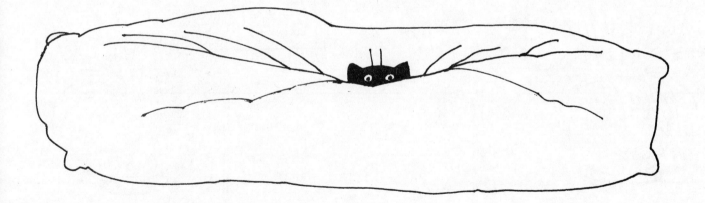

SIMON, WHO BECAME A DRUMMER IN A HEAVY
METAL ROCK BAND...

SIR J. WIMPEY BARRINGTON'S MOUNTAIN CLIMBING
EXPEDITION WAS ABOUT TO TAKE A MEMORABLE
TURN OF EVENTS .....

THREE CATS ON THE CONTINUAL QUEST FOR MORE FOOD...

TIDDLES LIKES TO WATCH T·V· BUT COMPLAINS ALOT!

CYRANO DE BERGERCAT...

TWO CATS DOING A JOGGING SUIT JOKE...

PUSS IN BOOTS: JOGGING

FIND THE CAT...

RUSSIAN CAT DOLLS..

MARVO THE MAGICIAN

GAMBLING CATS...

KANNY KAT...

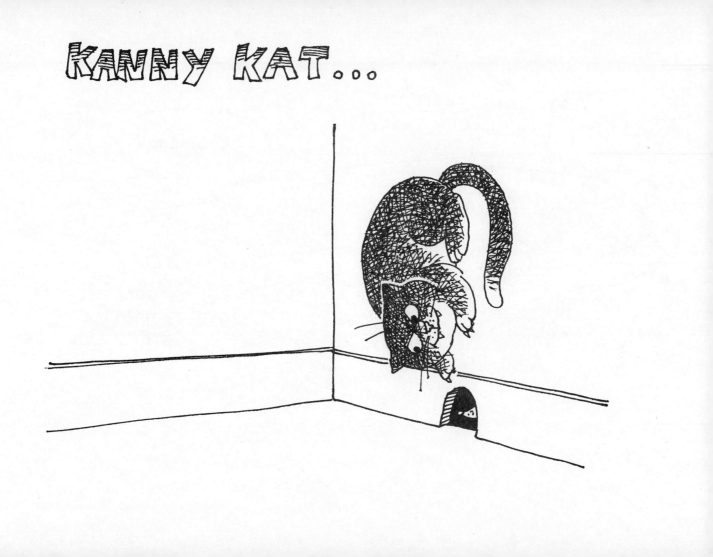

A CAT PROTECTING HIS MISTRESS'S MODESTY..

STRANGE PLACES CATS CHOOSE TO SLEEP...

DR STANISLAUS P SCHMENDERIK ATTEMPTING
A CAT·SMUGGLING DIVERSIONARY RUSE AT CUSTOMS...

MARIO CHOOSES A TIE...

HECTOR THE INSPECTOR
HUNTS FOR CAT-BURGLARS.....

SPOT THE CAT·BURGLAR...

SADDAM: A BAD PUSSY CAT

THIS IS FELIX, A DRUMMER WHO HAS BEEN TAKING
SUBSTANCES EXTRA TO HIS CAT FOOD...

TIDDLES, HAVING AN OUT-OF·CAT EXPERIENCE...

A CAT BURGER